K Clemens Costa was born in Dubuque, Iowa. Growing up on a cattle and crop farm meant early mornings, hard work, big gardens, and fresh, homegrown food. Farm life instilled an appreciation of Mother Nature, our natural resources, and what can come from the soil, if nurtured. Karin and her husband, Ron, currently grow produce on 120 acres in St. Paul, Minnesota.

GROWING FRENCH FRIES

Ordering Information:
Quantity sales: special discounts are available on quantity purchases by corporations, associations, and others. For details, contact the publisher at the address below.

Publisher's Cataloging-in-Publication data
Costa, K Clemens
Growing French Fries

ISBN 9781645755456 (Paperback)
ISBN 9781645755463 (Hardback)
ISBN 9781645755470 (ePub e-book)

Library of Congress Control Number: 2020912077

www.austinmacauley.com/us

First Published (2020)
Austin Macauley Publishers LLC
40 Wall Street, 28th Floor
New York, NY 10005
USA
mail-usa@austinmacauley.com
+1 (646) 5125767

This book is dedicated to my dad, Bill Clemens. He was a crop, hog, and cattle farmer his entire life. He loved raising show cattle, had a passion for the New York Yankees and NASCAR races, and was dedicated to his family. He truly enjoyed the beauty of his farmland, the rolling hills, the sounds of the creek, and time spent with his loved ones.

I would like to thank my two daughters, Gina and Grace, for pushing me to tell this story. They have read many rewrites, encouraged me during this long process, and have given me so much inspiration.

A French fry... so tasty; a perfect and golden stick.
Dip it in ketchup. Now, give it a lick!

But where does a plate of start?
Have you ever wondered about that part?

How do get on grocery store racks?
Or in fast food restaurants piled up in stacks?

Is it the grocery clerk? The cook? Who is responsible for this feat?
It's a farmer, like Farmer Billie, who grows your French fry treat!

FRENCH FRIES
FRENCH FRIES
FRENCH FRIES
FRENCH FRIES.
FRENCH FRIES

But don't grow on stalks, on bushes, or on a tree.
Fries start out as something else. Look and you will see!

This right here is what will turn into your fries.
Those crispy treats are just potatoes in disguise.

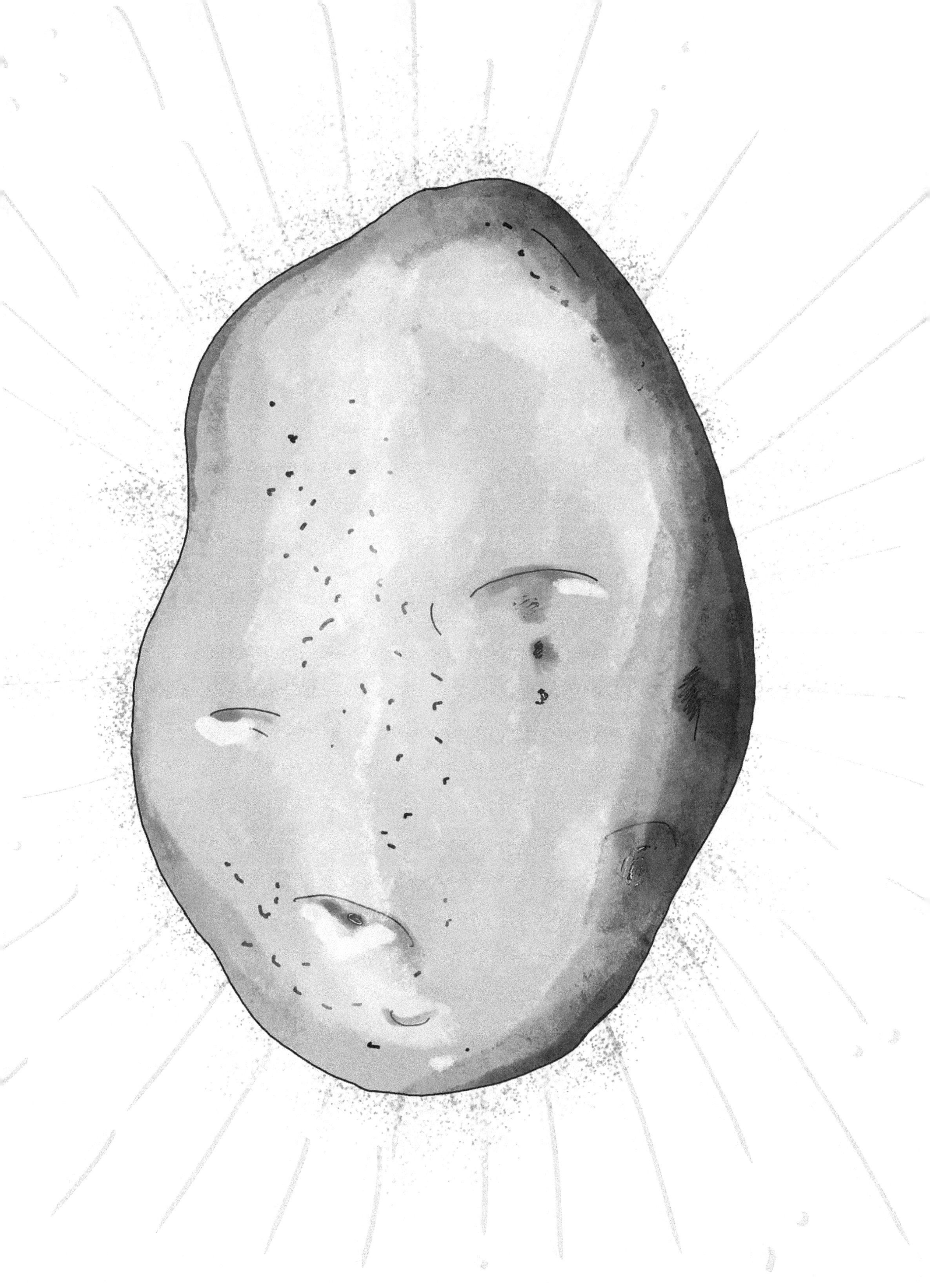

A farmer grows your food, you know.
With his hands, dirt, seeds, and a hoe!

Each year, April's rain falls and warms the soil that is cold and bare.
This is nature's way of telling farmers it's time to prepare.

APRIL
S M T W TH F S
16 17 18 19
21 22 23 24 25
28 29 30
SEED
POTATOES

Look! Out of the barn Farmer Billie drives his red tractor.
Revving it up loud, he has unplowed fields to get after.

He steers the plow down and back for most of the hot day.
Which turns the bumpy ground upside-down along the way.

Farmer Billie plants the potatoes and spaces them just right.
He pushes the dirt up and over which covers them up tight.

NY
SEED
POTATOES
SEED
POTATOES
SEED
POTATOES

Along with the potato plants that grow,
pesky weeds have appeared.
These unwanted plants steal water and nutrients;
they must be cleared.

Farmer Billie inches the pointy cultivator,
very slowly and carefully down each row.
It pulls up the weeds which allow the young potato
plants to breathe, stretch, and grow.

Months go by and the plants turn a yellow hue.
Farmer Billie sharpens his shovels as this is his cue.

It is finally time to start digging up the field!
Farmer Billie's excited to uncover his yield.

Big potatoes here and smaller potatoes there.
Holy cow, there are potatoes everywhere!

Working morning till night, he gets them all dug up.
The harvest is complete.
Farmer Billie's jeans are dirty,
his cap is dusty, and he is beat!

NY

Hooray! He gets his fresh potatoes all packed,
stacked, and on the road.
He drives straight to the factory without losing any of his load.

TOCK CAR RACES EVERY SUNDAY,
6PM!DUBUQUE FAIRGROUNDS

Farmer Billie pulls in and meets the owner on the street.
One look and she says, "Let's turn these taters into a treat!"

The skins get properly washed, scrubbed, and peeled.
Sliced into sticks, and look, at what is revealed?

The potatoes have gotten their tasty disguise!

They have now been transformed into golden

But wait!...Where's the ketchup?

FARMER PETE

CPSIA information can be obtained
at www.ICGtesting.com
Printed in the USA
LVHW070853230920
666824LV00004B/293